For alec · billy · callum

ISBN 0-590-48218-1

 Published by Scholastic Inc., 555 Broadway, New York, NY 10012, by arrangement with Bradbury Press, Macmillan Publishing Company.

12 11 10 9 8 7 6 5 4 3 5 6 7 8 9/9

Printed in the U.S.A. 14

First Scholastic printing, March 1994

ANIMAL PARADE

Jakki Wood

SCHOLASTIC INC.
New York Toronto London Auckland Sydney

Aa aardvark • antelopes • anteater • ants

Bb beaver • bison • bear • bee • butterflies

Cc camel • chimpanzee • caterpillar • crab •

coyote • cockatoo • crocodile • cheetah

Dd

dolphin • dromedary • duck • ducklings

Ee elephants • emu

Ff fly • flying fish • flamingos • frog • fox

Gg giraffes • grasshopper • gorilla

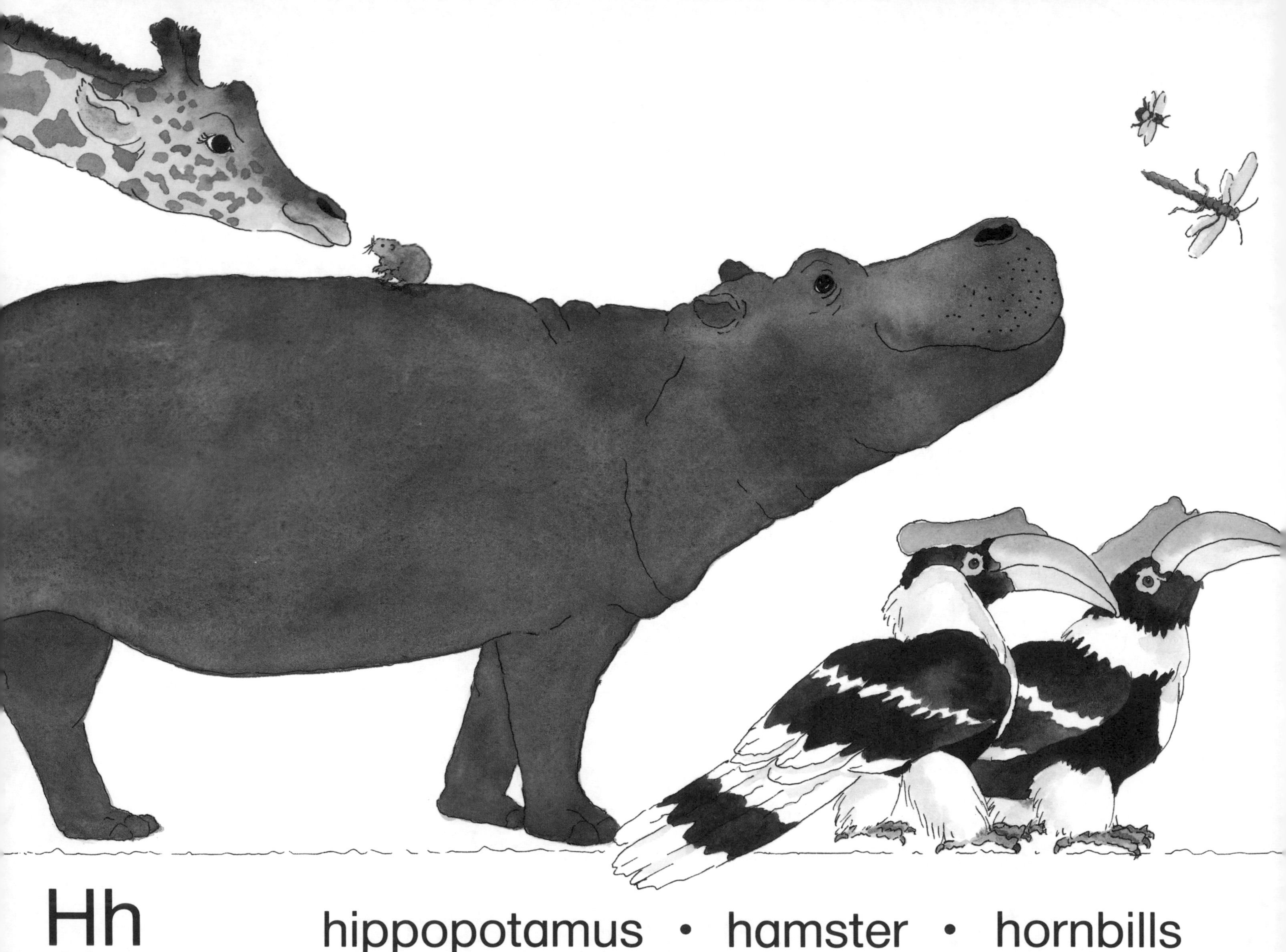

Hh hippopotamus • hamster • hornbills

Ii ibex • iguana • ibis • insects

Jj jaguar • joey

Kk kangaroo •

kittens • koalas • kookaburra • kiwis

Ll lemur • lion • llama • lynx • lizard

Mm moose • monkeys • mice • macaw

Nn narwhal • numbat Oo owl •

ostrich • octopus • orangutan • okapi

Pp

panda • pig • parrots

penguins • pelican • porcupine

Qq quetzals • quails • quokka • quoll

Rr raccoon • rhinoceros • rat • reindeer

Ss sea lion • shoebill • snails • skunk • snakes

Tt

tortoise • tiger • tapir

Uu umbrella bird • uakari

Vv vipers • vulture

Ww walrus • wombat • wolf • warthog

Xx ox • x-ray fish
Yy yapok • yak

Zz
zebra fish • zorilla • zebra